M000035723

# SRA OPEN COURT READING

# We See

A Division of The McGraw·Hill Companies

Columbus, Ohio

**www.sra4kids.com**

*SRA/McGraw-Hill*

*A Division of The **McGraw·Hill** Companies*

Copyright © 2002 by SRA/McGraw-Hill.

All rights reserved. Except as permitted under the United States Copyright Act, no part of this publication may be reproduced or distributed in any form or by any means, or stored in a database or retrieval system, without prior written permission from the publisher.

Printed in the United States of America.

Send all inquiries to:
SRA/McGraw-Hill
8787 Orion Place
Columbus, OH 43240-4027

ISBN 0-07-569871-4
10 11 12 DBH 10 09 08 07

The  is here.

van

We see the  .

stop sign

We see the  and the  .

cow

pig

5

We see the  .

truck

We see the  and the  .

bus

bicycle

7

We see .

Grandma